RUTH

RUTH

FROM THE STORY TOLD IN THE BOOK OF RUTH

MAUD and MISKA PETERSHAM

THE MACMILLAN COMPANY, NEW YORK • COLLIER-MACMILLAN LIMITED, LONDON

The Macmillan Company, New York
Collier-Macmillan Canada, Ltd., Toronto, Ontario

Library of Congress catalog card number: 58-11303

Printed in the United States of America
New printing, 1958
Second Printing, 1967

CONTENTS

The land of Canaan was divided among the twelve tribes of Israel. These tribes had rulers called judges.

THE GIRL OF MOAB

NOW it came to pass in the days when the judges ruled in Judah there was a famine in that land. So a certain man of Bethlehem in Judah took his wife and his two sons and went to live in another land.

The name of the man was Elimelech and the name of his wife, Naomi.

They came into the country of Moab and dwelt there. Elimelech, the husband of Naomi, died and she and her two sons were left alone.

The two sons married women of the people of Moab. The name of the one was Orpah, and the name of the other was Ruth. Naomi and her sons and their wives dwelt in Moab about ten years.

Then both of Naomi's sons died, and she was left in a strange land without sons or husband.

Naomi longed to return to her own land. She had heard that the famine there was past and that now there was food in plenty. So she left the place where she was, and her two daughters-in-law went with her. They were on the way to return to the land of Judah.

Then Naomi told her two daughters-in-law not to go with her but to return each to her own mother's house. She asked God to be kind to them as they had been kind to her two sons and to her.

Then she kissed them, and they lifted up their voice and wept. And they said to her, "Surely we will return with thee unto thy people."

Again Naomi urged them to go back to their own people in the country of Moab.

At last Orpah kissed her mother-in-law and turned back, but Ruth would not leave her.

Then Naomi said, "Behold, thy sister-in-law is gone back unto her people, and unto her gods. Return thou after thy sister-in-law."

And Ruth said, "Entreat me not to leave thee, or to return from following after thee: for whither thou goest, I will go; and where thou lodgest, I will lodge: thy people shall be my people, and thy God my God: Where thou diest, will I die, and there will I be buried."

When Naomi saw that Ruth would not leave her, she said no more.

So they two went until they came to Bethlehem in Judah.

RUTH IN THE HARVEST FIELD

IT happened when they were come to Bethlehem that the people of the city came and said, "Is this Naomi?"

And she told them not to call her Naomi. She said to call her Mara, which means bitter, for God had dealt bitterly with her. She was sad, for she was now without husband and sons.

When Ruth and Naomi came to Bethlehem, it was the beginning of the barley harvest. Ruth went into the harvest field to gather the grain which the reapers had left behind them.

It so happened that the field into which she went belonged to a man of great wealth, whose name was Boaz. This man was a kinsman of Elimelech, Naomi's husband, who had died in the country of Moab.

While Ruth was gleaning in the field, Boaz came from Bethlehem. He said to his reapers, "The Lord be with you." And they answered, "The Lord bless thee."

Then Boaz saw Ruth gathering the grain, and he asked the servant that was set over the reapers who the maiden was.

The servant who was set over the reapers answered and said that it was she who had come back with Naomi out of the country of Moab. The servant told Boaz that she had asked that she might glean and gather the grain after the reapers. And he said, "She has been there from the morning until now."

Boaz himself then spoke to Ruth. He told her to remain in his field and not to go away, but to stay near his maidens and go with them wherever they were reaping. He said that no one would harm her and that when she was thirsty, she should drink from the jars of water which his servants had drawn from the well.

Then Ruth bowed herself to the ground and said to him, "Why have I found grace in thine eyes, that thou shouldest take knowledge of me, seeing I am a stranger?"

Boaz answered and said that he knew all she had done for her mother-in-law. He knew how she had left her own father and mother and her own land and had come to live among a strange people. He knew that she had put her trust in their God. And he asked the God of Israel to grant her a full reward.

Then she said, "Let me find favour in thy sight, my lord, for that thou hast comforted me, and for that thou hast spoken friendly unto thine handmaid."

And Boaz told her to come at mealtimes and eat the bread and dip her piece of bread in the sour wine. And Ruth sat beside the reapers, and Boaz gave her of the dried grain to eat. When she had eaten all that she wanted, she left.

And when she was risen up to glean, Boaz commanded his young men, saying, "Let her glean even among the sheaves, and reproach her not. And let fall also some of the handfuls of purpose for her, and leave them, that she may glean them, and rebuke her not."

So Ruth gleaned in the field until the evening and she beat out the grain she had gleaned. It was about an ephah of barley. She took it up and went into the city and showed her mother-in-law what she had gleaned.

When Ruth told Naomi in whose field she had gathered the grain, Naomi was glad and told her that Boaz was a near kinsman. She said it was good for her to stay in the fields of Boaz with his maidens.

So Ruth gathered grain with the maidens of Boaz until the end of the barley harvest and the wheat harvest. And she dwelt with her mother-in-law.

BOAZ AND RUTH

AT the end of the harvest, Boaz held a feast at the threshing floor. Naomi told Ruth to go to the threshing floor, and after the feast, when all was quiet, to lie down at the feet of Boaz.

Ruth did as Naomi told her. When Boaz slept, she came softly and lay down on the straw at his feet.

And it came to pass at midnight that Boaz awoke and saw someone lying at his feet. He asked who she was, and Ruth answered, "I am Ruth, thine handmaid." And Boaz said, "Blessed be thou of the Lord."

There was a custom in those times in the land of Israel that if a woman's husband were dead, the nearest kinsman of her husband might buy all that belonged to the husband and might take the woman as his wife.

Boaz wished Ruth as his wife. But though he was a near kinsman, there was one still nearer than he.

So in the morning Boaz went up to the gate of the city and sat down there. Soon this nearest kinsman came by, and Boaz spoke with him. Ten elders of the city came by and sat down with them. Then Boaz told them the story of Naomi and her daughter-in-law, Ruth.

When the kinsman had heard that story, he told Boaz and the elders that he would not ask his right as nearest kinsman. So that right became the right of Boaz.

It was a custom in Israel that a man drew off his shoe and gave it to his neighbor to make sure something which was done. Therefore when Boaz was finished speaking, the kinsman said to him, "Buy it for thee." So he drew off his shoe.

Then Boaz made it known to the elders and all the people in the gate that he would buy all that belonged to Elimelech's son. He also said that he would take Ruth, the woman of Moab, as his wife.

So Boaz took Ruth and she was his wife, and she bore a son.

And the women of Bethlehem came to Naomi. They said, "Blessed be the Lord, which hath not left thee this day without a kinsman, that his name may be famous in Israel. For thy daughter-in-law, which loveth thee, which is better to thee than seven sons, hath borne him."

Naomi took the child and loved it and cared for it.

This boy, the son of Ruth and Boaz, was named Obed. When he grew up, he had a son called Jesse. And in turn, Jesse became the father of David, the king of Israel.